SPORTSMATHS

J. M. Jodey

Blond Educational

It is illegal to reproduce, except by special permission of the Copyright owners, any part of the text of this publication, or of the illustrations. Reproduction of this material by any duplication process whatsoever, without authorisation, is a violation of copyright.

Metricated edition

First published in Great Britain 1965 by Blond Educational.
This edition 1972 by Blond Educational, Iliffe House, Iliffe Avenue, Oadby, Leicester.
© Copyright 1965, 1972 J. Edmundson. Illustrations © Copyright 1971 Blond Educational.
Set in 'Monophoto' Baskerville by Cranmer Brown (Filmsetters) Ltd
Printed in Great Britain by Billing & Sons Ltd
Guildford and London
ISBN 0 219 51657 X

CONTENTS

(Central Press)

In 1971, Geoffrey Boycott, the Yorkshire opening batsman, became the first Englishman to average over 100 runs per innings during an English season.

1 CRICKET

Some Interesting Facts

Cricket was played in Surrey as long ago as 1598.

In 1948, D. C. S. Compton, playing for the M.C.C. in South Africa, scored 300 runs in 181 minutes.

The youngest player to play for a County side was W. W. F. Pullen of Gloucester. He was 15 years 11 months old when he played against Yorkshire in 1882.

How to Find a Batsman's Average

A batsman's average is found by adding together the number of runs made over several innings, and dividing this total by the number of completed innings. For example: a batsman scores 20, 60, 80 and 40 in four innings. His average is then:– $(20+60+80+40) \div 4$, which is $200 \div 4$. The average would then be 50 runs per innings.

But if, during an innings, a batsman is *not out*, the score he makes is added to the total number of runs, though the innings is not added to the divisor. Thus, if a batsman scores 20, 60 *not out*, 80 and 40 *not out*, his average would be 200 (the total number of runs) $\div 2$ (the number of *completed* innings). This gives an average of 100.

Exercises

1 In 1971, Geoffrey Boycott of Yorkshire became the first Englishman to record a batting average of over 100 in an English season. His County scores were: 61, 110, 30, 75, 88, 112 not out, 9, 169, 24, 121 not out, 233, 58, 182 not out, 6, 112, 13, 133, 34, 0, 33, 3, 169, 151, 40, 111, 14, 66, 138 not out, 84 and 124 not out.

a How many runs did Boycott score during the season?

b How many *completed* innings did he have?

c What was his average for the season? (Work to 2 decimal places).

2 A County team needs 180 runs in their second innings to win. There are exactly 120 minutes left for play. Batsman No. 1 scores at the rate of $1\frac{1}{2}$ runs every 2 minutes and his partner at the rate of $2\frac{1}{2}$ runs every 3 minutes. If they play out the full 120 minutes:–

a What will be the result of the match?

b How many runs will each batsman make?

3 In 1920 P. G. H. Fender of Surrey hit 100 runs in 35 minutes. In 1948 Dennis Compton scored 300 in 181 minutes. In 1938 Len Hutton scored 364 runs in 13 hours 20 minutes. In 1954 Hanif Mohammed took 7 hours 48 minutes to score 100.

What is each batsman's rate of scoring in runs per minute?

4 A completely circular cricket ground has a boundary circumference of 660 metres. A full size cricket pitch (20·12 metres) is placed centrally in the middle of the ground.

a How far is each wicket from the nearest point on the boundary?

b If an equal number of red, yellow and white flags are placed at 2 metre intervals round the boundary, how many are needed?

5 A school required the following items of equipment for the coming cricket season:

2 bats @ £4·25   2 bats @ £3·40
6 match balls @ £2·10   6 practice balls @ 75p
2 sets of pads @ £2·50 a set   1 set of wickets @ £1·75
1 pair of wicket-keeping gloves @ £3·75
2 pairs of batting gloves @ £1·15 a pair

a What is the total cost?

b How much money will the school save if it receives a 10% discount for prompt payment?

2 ASSOCIATION FOOTBALL

Some Interesting Facts

The most goals scored by a player in a single season is 82. This was done by W. R. (Dixie) Dean of Everton in the 1927/28 season. He scored 60 goals in League games, 3 in Cup Ties and 19 in representative matches.

The record number of goals scored by an individual in an International match is 6. This feat was achieved by J. Bambrick playing for Ireland against Wales in Belfast in 1930.

The fastest goal ever recorded was scored 4 seconds after the kick-off by J. Fryatt for Bradford against Tranmere Rovers in 1964.

The world record transfer fee was paid by Juventus of Turin for the Varese player Pietro Anastasi. Anastasi cost £400,000.

In 1889, Preston North End won the League Championship without losing a match and the Cup without having a goal scored against them.

In calculating League positions, the team with the highest number of points occupies the top place. The team with the next highest number occupies the second place, and so on. If two teams have an equal number of points, the higher position is taken by the team with the better goal average.

This is calculated by dividing the number of goals scored by a team by the number of goals scored against it. For example, one team has scored 50 goals and had 25 scored against it. The goal average is $50 \div 25$, which is 2. Another team has scored 60 goals and conceded 35. This time the average is $60 \div 35$, which is 1·71. As 2 is greater than 1·71, the team with this average would take the higher position.

(*Radio Times, Hulton Picture Library*)

A scene at the 1923 F.A. Cup Final – the first played at Wembley Stadium – when Bolton Wanderers beat West Ham United by 2 – 0. Before the match the crowd invaded the pitch and were driven back by mounted police.

Exercises

1 Football teams receive 2 points for a win, 1 for a draw and 0 if they lose. The table shows the records of six teams part way through a season, but the teams are not in the correct order. Work out what the order should be.

			HOME					AWAY			
	P	W	D	L	F	A	W	D	L	F	A
Watford	33	9	7	1	33	19	4	3	9	20	34
Bournemouth	33	11	6	0	33	11	4	7	5	22	23
Bristol City	33	11	1	4	41	14	7	4	6	29	30
Portsmouth	31	12	5	0	37	17	8	2	4	12	14
Grimsby	32	12	2	2	29	11	6	2	8	19	30
Reading	31	10	3	2	32	15	7	1	8	25	34

2 The attendances and 'gate' money at seven Fifth Round F.A. Cup matches were as follows:

Aston Villa v Charlton	42,200	£8,900
Blackburn v Middlesborough	32,700	£6,150
Liverpool v Preston	55,000	£10,500
West Brom v Tottenham	55,000	£10,000
Fulham v Port Vale	29,500	£5,000
Man. Utd. v Sheffield Wednesday	65,000	£12,000
Sheffield United v Norwich	49,600	£8,700

a   What was the total attendance at the seven matches?

b   What was the average attendance at each match?

c   What was the total 'gate' money?

d   What was the average cost to each spectator? (to the nearest p).

e   Use the last figure to calculate the gate money at the Everton v Burnley match which was watched by 52,000 spectators.

3 The diagram below shows half a soccer pitch. Draw the whole pitch to scale, using 10 metres = 4 centimetres or 20 metres = 4 centimetres (whichever is the most convenient).

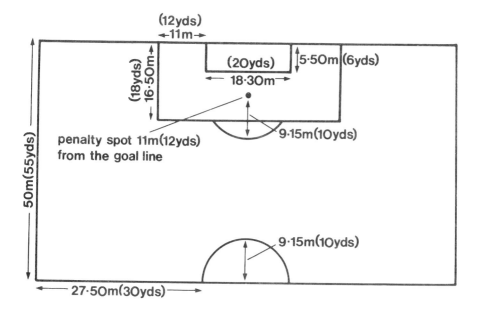

4 At the end of the football season, the head groundsman of the pitch in question 3 decides to returf the whole of both penalty areas and a strip right across the centre of the field, ten metres on each side of the centre line.

a   What is the total area to be re-turfed?

b   If each turf measures 1 metre by 50 centimetres, how many will be required?

c   If turves cost £4·50 per 100, what will be the total cost?

5 The area covered by grass at Wembley Stadium measures 114 metres by 78 metres. The actual pitch is 100 metres long by 72 metres wide.

a   If nine people can stand in one square metre, how many could stand in the whole grass area?

b   By experiment it has been found that twelve schoolboys can stand without undue discomfort in one square metre. How many could be accommodated on the pitch?

3 SWIMMING

Exercises

1 A simple but rough method of changing yards into metres is to subtract $\frac{1}{10}$ of the number of yards. For example: How many metres are equal to 200 yards? $200 - \left(\frac{200}{10}\right) = 200 - 20 = 180$ metres.

In a 50 yard bath John Brown swam two lengths in 52·5 seconds. Later, in a 100 metre race he was credited with a time of 58·3 seconds. In which of the two races did he swim the faster?

2 The first man to swim the Channel was Captain Matthew Webb, who, in 1875 swam an estimated distance of 60 kilometres (to make the 34 kilometre crossing) in a time of 21 hours, 45 minutes. In 1950, an Egyptian swimmer made the crossing in 10 hours, 50 minutes.

a How long, to the nearest minute, did Webb take to swim each kilometre?

b If he had swum the 34 kilometres direct at the same speed, by how much would he have been faster than the Egyptian?

3 In the final of a 4×100 metre relay race four teams each of four swimmers take part. The times of each swimmer are shown below.

	1ST	2ND	3RD	4TH
Team A	55·6	54·8	54·7	53·9
Team B	54·5	55·2	55·7	54·9
Team C	53·9	54·3	56·2	54·4
Team D	55·1	55·4	53·9	54·0

a Which team was leading at 300 metres?

b Which team won the race and by how many seconds?

c What was the finishing order?

d What was the average time for each swimmer in the winning team?

11

(*Associated Press*)

Felipe Munoz (top) of Mexico touches a fraction of a second ahead of Vladimir Kosinsky of Russia, to take the gold medal in the 200 metres breaststroke in the Mexico Olympics, 1968.

4   An American, John V. Sigmund, in 1940 swam 470 kilometres down the Mississippi River at an average time of $11\frac{1}{2}$ minutes per kilometre. How long did it take him to complete his swim?

5   A swimming bath is slowly heated over several days. The attendant only has a Fahrenheit thermometer, although his records must be entered up in degrees Centigrade. Daily readings were: 41°, 45°, 50°, 55°, 59°, 68° and 77°. Convert these temperatures into degrees Centigrade (to the nearest °C).

Notes:
1   To change degrees Fahrenheit to degrees Centigrade:
subtract 32 and then *multiply* by $\frac{5}{9}$.
For example: Change 50° Fahrenheit to degrees Centigrade
$(50-32) = 18$ $18 \times \frac{5}{9} = \frac{90}{9} = 10$.
Thus 50° Fahrenheit = 10° Centigrade.
2   To change degrees Centigrade to degrees Fahrenheit:
multiply by $\frac{9}{5}$ and then *add* 32.
For example: Change 25° Centigrade to degrees Fahrenheit
$25 \times \frac{9}{5} = 45$ $(45+32) = 77$.
Thus 25° Centigrade = 77° Fahrenheit.

---

4 MAKING GRAPHS

A graph is a mathematical 'picture' which presents facts and figures in a simple clear form. A graph can be made in a number of different ways.

Problem

1   The attendances at the first six matches of a First Division Football Club were as follows: 15,000, 17,000, 20,000, 18,000, 22,000 and 28,000. Show these attendances by means of a graph.

Method 1

Draw a straight line AB along the bottom edge of your graph paper. Mark off six equal spaces as shown in the illustration on p. 14. Draw a vertical axis AC, and write the figure '14,000' at the point where the two axes intersect. At equal intervals up the vertical axis write 15,000, 16,000, and so on, up to 28,000. Now mark in the attendances for each match. The final result is a graph showing, at a glance, the rise and fall in attendances.

Method 2

Another method of showing the attendance figures is to use a block graph. Draw and shade vertical columns as shown in the illustration on p. 15. Additional facts can be written in to explain the reasons for very low or very high attendance.

Exercises

Using either of the above methods, draw graphs to show:
1   The attendance at six Rugby League matches:
   8,000, 7,500, 8,200, 9,100, 5,600, 6,000.

2   The 'gate' money at six football matches:
   £1,500, £1,700, £1,650, £1,800, £900, £850.

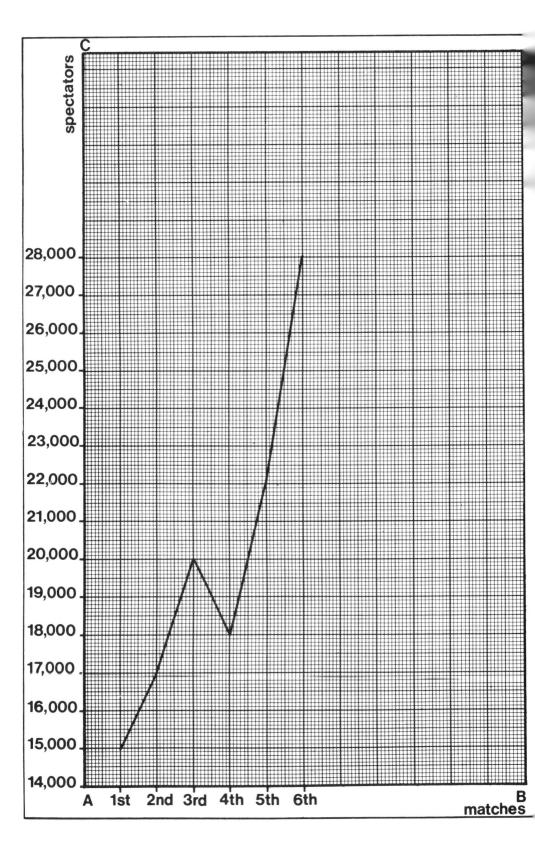

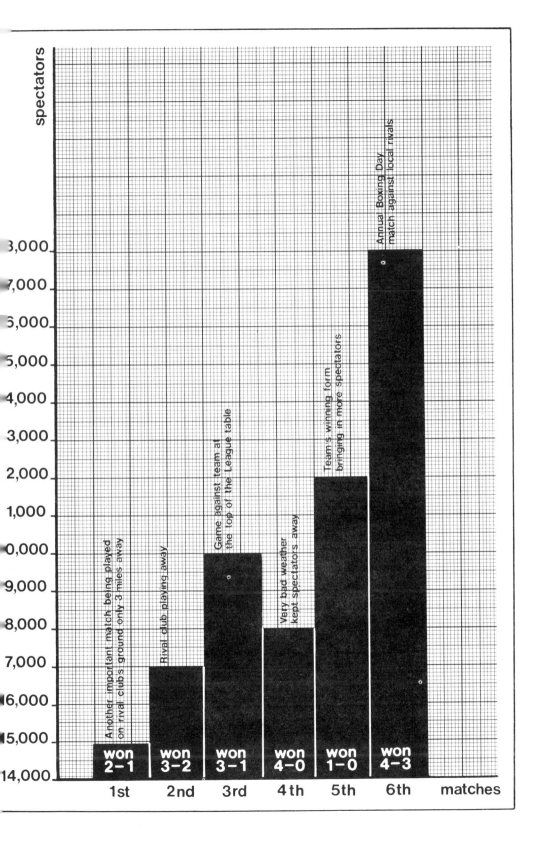

3 The runs scored by a County cricketer in fifteen innings:
25, 54, 32, 104, 96, 108, 73, 10, 0, 39, 63, 85, 105, 90, 120.

4 The best heights cleared by a high jumper in twenty recorded training sessions over the summer season:

1m 80cm	1m 75cm	1m 85cm	1m 88cm	1m 90cm
1m 95cm	1m 90cm	1m 98cm	1m 98cm	1m 95cm
1m 98cm	2m 00cm	2m 02cm	1m 99cm	2m 04cm
2m 00cm	2m 05cm	2m 08cm	2m 02cm	2m 10cm

5 The distances thrown in ten competitions by a javelin thrower:

62·55m	66·33m	67·14m	67·10m	69·75m
70·35m	72·90m	74·20m	79·50m	80·20m

6 The figures below the results of ten matches played by the Penniwistle Secondary School Basketball team. Their score is given first in each case. On the same graph show the points scored by the Penniwistle team *and* their opponents. Two lines will have to be drawn. Use a different colour for the second line.

Results:	36 – 24	18 – 26	24 – 20	40 – 22	50 – 30
	48 – 20	39 – 18	28 – 30	46 – 10	52 – 26

5 PITCHES AND COURTS

Drawing to Scale

The drawings on this page and the next two pages give details of pitches for three games, but in two cases only half the pitch is shown, the other half, of course, is exactly the same.

Draw, in each case, the full pitch to a scale which will enable you to get a complete drawing on a page of your exercise book or on a sheet of foolscap paper.

In each case a suitable scale is suggested.

Association Football pitch ⎫
Rugby League pitch (overleaf) ⎭

Suggested scale
1 centimetre = 5 metres

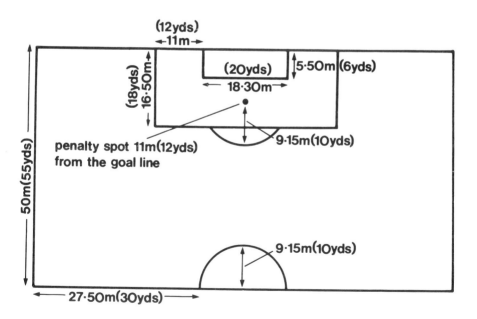

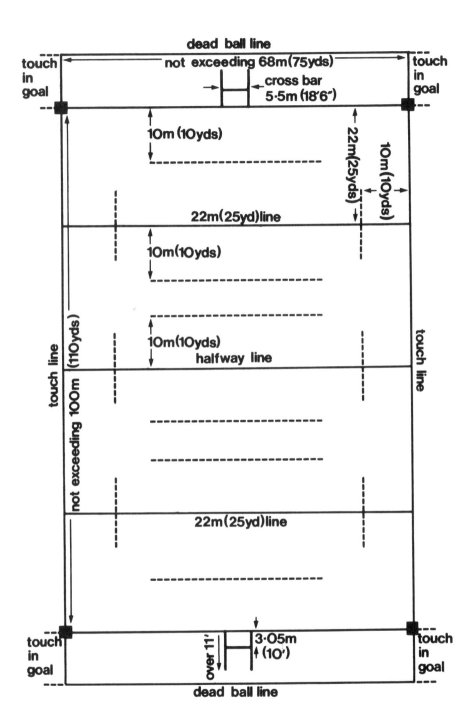

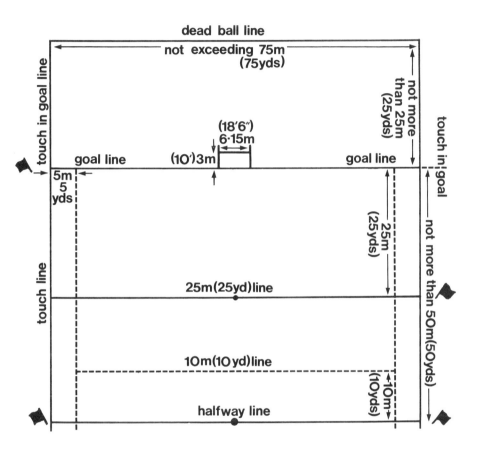

6   SHOWING SPEED BY GRAPH

Speed can also be shown graphically. Look at the graph shown on the opposite page.

Speeds from 0 to 90 kilometres per hour (kph) are shown on the vertical axis. A time of one hour, marked in ten minute intervals is shown on the horizontal axis.

The continuous unbroken line shows the performance of a cyclist who travels at a steady speed of 32kph. The broken line shows the performance of a car that travels at a speed of 90kph.

Copy the graph on a sheet of squared centimetre graph paper, then show the following speeds on the same sheet:

1 a   8kph   b   24kph   c   72kph

   d   72 kilometres travelled in $1\frac{1}{2}$ hours.

   e   96 kilometres travelled in 2 hours.

   f   80 kilometres travelled in 30 minutes.

2   What do you notice about the angles of the lines you have drawn on your graph. How can you tell at a glance which is the fastest speed?

By using graphs of this type, simple problems involving speed can be solved. Look at the following problem:

A cyclist starts from town A and cycles towards town B which is a distance of 48 kilometres away. He cycles steadily at 24kph. A quarter of an hour later a motorist leaves town A for town B and travels at 48kph.

At what time will he catch the cyclist up and how many miles will they be from their starting point?

20

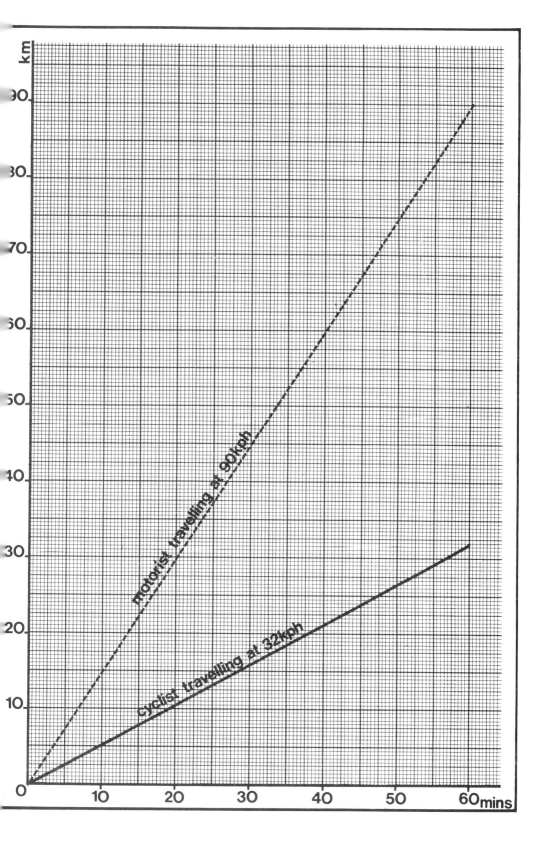

Method

Mark out a sheet of graph paper as shown in the illustration opposite. Draw in the line representing the speed of the cyclist (24kph). Next draw in the line representing the speed of the motorist (48kph), but begin his line at the 15-minute mark, as shown. You will notice that at one point the two lines cross each other.

If you have drawn your lines accurately, you will find that the point of intersection is at the point representing 12 kilometres on the vertical scale and 30 minutes on the horizontal scale. The answers to the questions then are:

a   The motorist will catch up with the cyclist 30 minutes after the cyclist left town A and 15 minutes after he himself left town A.

b   The point of overtaking will be exactly 12km from town A.

Now, using the same methods, try to work out the answers to the following problems:

1   A cyclist leaves town A for town B and travels at 32kph. Thirty minutes later a motorist leaves town A travelling at 64kph. How many minutes will it take for the motorist to catch up with the cyclist, and how many kilometres has the cyclist travelled?

2   A motorist leaves town C and drives at 72 kph. 15 minutes later another motorist leaves the same town and travels in the same direction at 96kph. How many kilometres will the first motorist have travelled before he is overtaken by the second?

3   A walker leaves town A and sets off towards the coast at 84kph. Half an hour later a cyclist leaves along the same road travelling steadliy at 24kph. Half an hour after the cyclist has left, a motorist

a   How many kilometres from town A will the cyclist pass the walker?

b   How many kilometres from town A will the motorist pass the walker?

c   How many kilometres from town A will the motorist pass the cyclist?

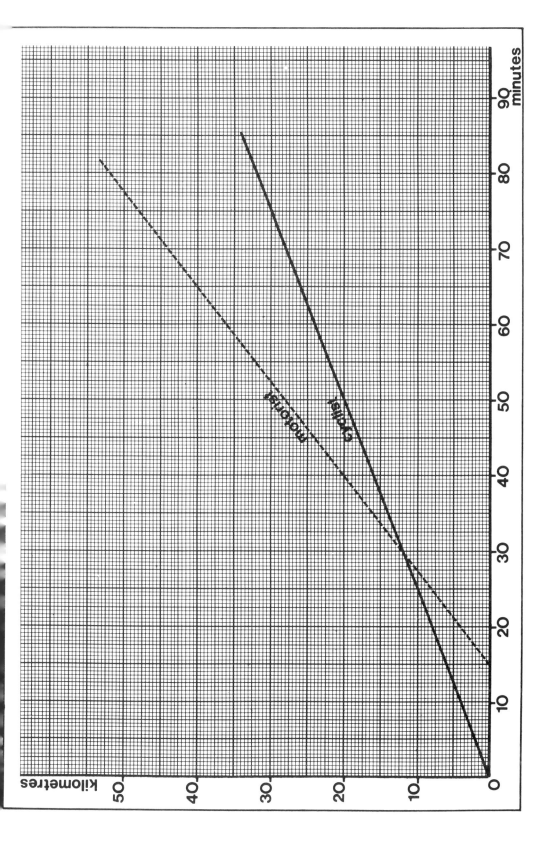

In all the problems discussed so far we have assumed that the travellers moved steadily and did not stop on the way. But suppose, for instance that a walker decides to rest for ten minutes at the end of an hour, or that the cyclist had a puncture and stopped to mend it for fifteen minutes. How would you show these on a graph?

Look at the graph on the opposite page. The walker, shown by the dotted line, walks for one hour then rests for ten minutes. The rest period is shown by the horizontal line between A and B.

The line is horizontal because although the walker is not moving, *time is still going on*, and at the end of his rest 70 minutes have passed since he started walking. At the end of his rest the walker carries on at his steady speed of 8kph.

The continuous unbroken line shows a similar picture. A cyclist travels for an hour at a speed of 32kph and then has a puncture. He takes 15 minutes (shown by the horizontal line between A and B) to mend the puncture and then he continues at 32kph.

Problems

Mark out a sheet of graph paper as shown in the illustration opposite. Draw the following graphs on the same sheet:
4 A motorist travels at 48kph for 20 minutes, and then stops at a garage for petrol. This takes 5 minutes. He then continues his journey travelling at a speed of 72kph. If he started out at 10 a.m., at what time would he reach a point 96km from his starting point?

5 A racing motorist starts off in a race averaging a speed of 150kph, but after only fifteen minutes he has to pull into the pits for an adjustment to his brakes. This takes five minutes. On rejoining the race, his speed is reduced to 120kph. If the race started at mid-day, at what time would he pass the 70 kilometre mark?

6 A racing cyclist enters an 80km time trial which starts at 6 a.m. After racing for 2 hours at 30kph, he has a puncture and takes 3 minutes to change his wheel. In the next half hour he covers 15km, then has another puncture. This time he changes his wheel in only 2 minutes and then sprints to the finish at a speed of 40kph, At what time did he finish the race? (to the nearest minute).

24

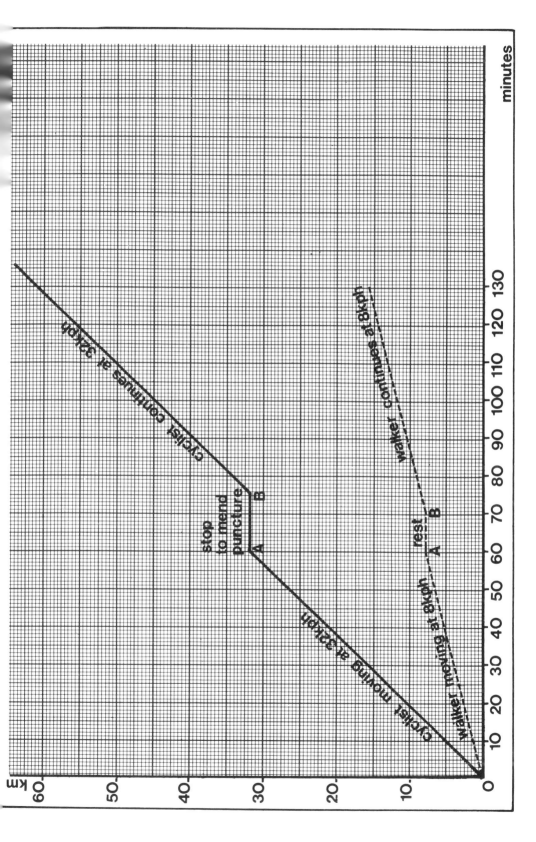

7 SHOWING RACES BY GRAPH

In a 100 metre race at the White City, London, a competitor named Black ran the distance in 11 seconds. Another competitor, White, took exactly 12 seconds. By how many metres did Black beat White?

Mark out your graph paper to show 12 seconds along the horizontal axis and 100 metres up the vertical axis. Next draw in the line representing Black's speed of 11 seconds for 100 metres (line A). Draw in the line B showing White's speed of 12 seconds for the 100 metres.

If you look at the two lines you have drawn you will see that point A (when Black finished) is vertically above a point on White's line. The distance AD represents a distance of almost exactly 8 metres. In other words, when Black finished White had covered only 92 metres of the race, and Black therefore won by 8 metres.

The last 10 metres and last second of the race are drawn in the square inset to twice the scale to show this point more clearly.

1   In the European Championships 200 metre race the winner's time was 19·0 seconds. If the time of the sixth competitor was 20·0 seconds, how many metres had he run when the winner crossed the finishing line?

2   Two racing motor-cyclists are timed over a distance of 2 kilometres. The first takes exactly 30 seconds, the second, 28 seconds. By how many metres did the second rider win?

3   In a race over 40,000 metres the winner averaged 17kph and the second 16kph. What was the time of the winner (to the nearest minute) and by what distance did he beat the second man (to the nearest 400 metres)?

4   In a similar race to the one above, a competitor ran 18 kilometres in the first hour then was seized by cramp, which held him up for 6 minutes. On recovering, he continued the race at a steady 16kph. Find out his time to the nearest minute.

26

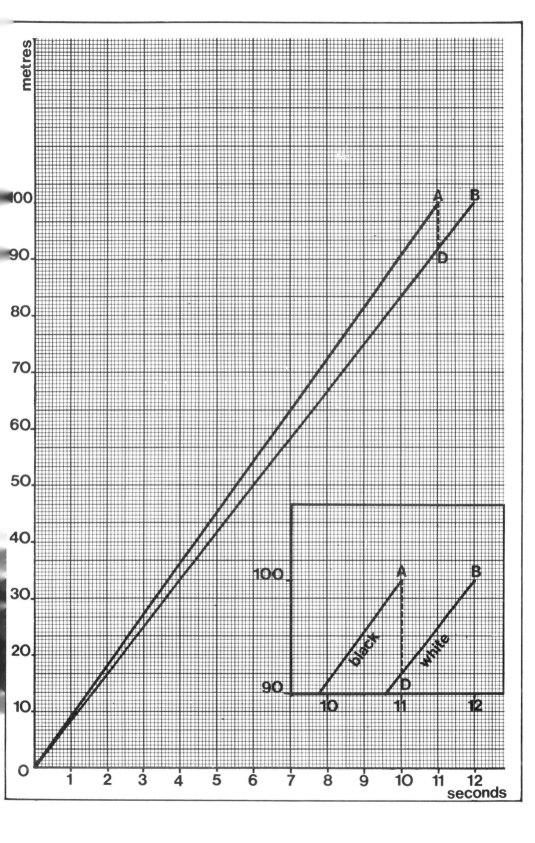

8 ASSOCIATION FOOTBALL

Some Interesting Facts

A form of football was played as early as 1530 in Florence in Italy. Each team consisted of 26 players.

The earliest reference in Great Britain was in 1672 when a print showing football being played in Edinburgh was published.

The highest number of goals scored in a League match is 17, scored in 1935 when Tranmere Rovers beat Oldham Athletic by 13 goals to 4.

The highest number of goals scored by an individual player in a League match is 10. These were scored in 1936 by J. Payne, playing for Luton Town against Bristol Rovers.

The largest number of full English International Caps won by any player is 106 by Bobby Charlton of Manchester United.

The biggest crowd ever to watch a football match is 200,000, who paid £125,000 to see Brazil play Uruguay in Rio de Janeiro in 1950.

The longest ever F.A. Cup Tie was played between Stoke City and Bury in 1955. After four draws, Stoke won by 3 goals to 2 in the fifth match. The teams played for a total of 9 hours 22 minutes.

The longest single game of football was played in Brazil between Santos, Brazil and Penarol Football Club of Montevideo. The game started at 9.30 p.m. and did not finish until 1.00 a.m., three and a half hours later.

The youngest player ever to play in a First Division game is Derek Foster who kept goal for Sunderland on August 22, 1964. Derek was only fifteen years old.

Exercises

1 The attendances at the First Division games of the Football League on the opening day of the 1970–1971 season were as follows:

Burnley v. Liverpool (26,702) Chelsea v. Derby (46,969)
Everton v. Arsenal (49,684) Huddersfield v. Blackpool (22,787)
Manchester United v. Leeds (59,365) Newcastle v. Wolves (38,320)
Nottingham Forest v. Coventry (25,137) Stoke v. Ipswich (18,000)
Southampton v. Manchester City (24,699)
Tottenham v. West Ham (53,640)
West Bromwich Albion v. Crystal Palace (24,766)

a What was the total attendance at the 11 matches?

b What was the average attendance at each match?

c If the average cost of admission was 40p, what was the total amount of 'gate' money taken (to the nearest £1)?

2 One Saturday 144 goals were scored in the Football League. Assume that all the games started at 3 p.m. and lasted 90 minutes. Calculate how often, on average, a goal was scored during the afternoon.

3 A football club bought a new striker for a fee of £30,000. Their average 'gate' is 24,000 at 40p each, and this just covers their normal expenses. If the club have 20 home games to play, by how many spectators per match must their 'gate' be increased to pay for the new player?

4 A P.E. master takes a party of 40 boys to an International match at Wembley. The normal single fare from their town to Wembley is 80p. The tickets for the match cost 50p each. By buying a party ticket, however, the fare for the boys is only three-quarters of the single fare for the double journey and, for the master, single fare plus one-half for the double journey. Find out the total cost for the whole outing.

5 Eleven players in a football team each receive a basic £30 per week in wages, with a bonus of £8 for a win and £4 for a draw. After ten weeks of the season the team have won six games, drawn four and lost two. How much money does the club pay altogether in wages and bonuses during this period?

9 RUGBY UNION FOOTBALL

(Central Press)

A scene from the 1971 Lions' tour of New Zealand. The Lions won the Test series by two matches to one, with one drawn.

Some Interesting Facts

Rugby Union football is said to have originated at Rugby School in 1823 when William Webb Ellis 'picked up a ball and ran'.

The highest score in an International match was when France beat Rumania in the 1924 Olympic Games by 61 points to 3.

The New Zealand International Rugby team, during a tour of Australia, beat Northern New South Wales by 103 points to nil.

The longest drop goal was kicked by G. Brand of South Africa playing against England at Twickenham in 1932. The distance was 90 yards.

Exercises

1   In Rugby Union Football a try counts three points. If the try is converted two more points are scored. A penalty goal scores 2 points and a dropped goal the same number.

In a game between London Welsh and the Wasps, London Welsh scored four tries (two of which were converted), two dropped goals and two penalty goals. The Wasps scored three tries (all converted), three dropped goals and one penalty goal. What was the final score?

2   The diagram below gives the approximate metric measurements of a typical Rugby Union pitch. Draw this to a scale of 10m = 1cm.

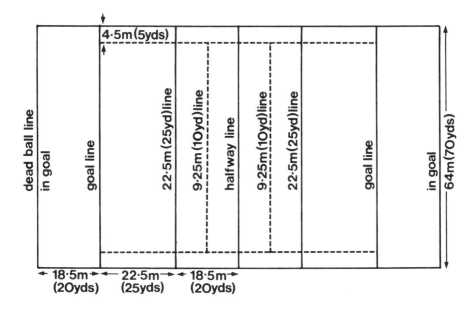

3   In the pitch shown above:

a   What is the area of the pitch between the goal lines?

b   What is the total area of the whole field?

c   The groundsman decides to re-turf the centre of the pitch between the two 22·5 metres lines. Each turf measures 1 metre by 40 centimetres. How many turves will he need?

4 A rugby club secretary buys 18 shirts @ £2·50 each; 18 pairs of shorts @ £1·50 a pair; 18 pairs of stockings @ £0·75 a pair and four rugby balls @ £5·26 each.

a   What is the total cost of the equipment?

b   If the forty members of the club pay a special levy of £1·50 towards the cost, how much must the secretary find?

5 Below are given the playing records of eight leading Rugby Union Football clubs part was through a season. *Assuming* that these clubs were playing in a League Competition, and knowing that they gained 2 points for a win, 1 for a draw and 0 for a defeat, arrange the teams in correct League order.

CLUB	PLAYED	WON	DRAWN	LOST	POINTS
Wasps	20	10	4	6	?
London Welsh	22	12	5	5	?
Harlequins	20	9	2	9	?
Bedford	19	9	3	7	?
Headingley	18	10	2	6	?
Richmond	20	12	2	6	?
Llanelli	21	11	3	7	?
Penryn	20	13	2	5	?

10 BOXING

Some Interesting Facts

A form of boxing was one of the events in the ancient Olympic Games as long ago as 776 B.C.

The longest recorded fight in which gloves were used took place between two Americans–Andy Bowen and Jack Burke, in 1893. The fight lasted for 110 rounds and took 7 hours, 4 minutes. Neither won, as the fight was declared 'no contest'.

The longest period which any man has held the World Heavyweight Championship is 11 years, 8 months and 9 days by Joe Louis who held the title between 1937 and 1950.

The youngest man ever to win the World Heavyweight Championship was Floyd Patterson, who was only 21 years, 10 months old when he won the title in 1956.

In 1888 two boxers, Cal McCarthy and Jimmy Reagan, bumped their heads together in the 77th round of a contest and knocked each other out.

Henry Armstrong ('Homicide Hank') is the only boxer ever to have held world titles at *three weights simultaneously*. From August to December 1938 he was Featherweight, Lightweight and Welterweight Champion of the World.

Abraham Hollandersky (Abe the Newsboy) had 1309 fights between 1905 and 1918. In addition he took part in 387 wrestling bouts.

Pat Floyd won his first ABA Heavyweight Championship in 1929 and his fourth 17 years later in 1946.

Exercises

During a period of six weeks training for a contest, a boxer runs on the road every day except Sundays. During the first week he runs eight kilometres each day, and he increases this distance by one kilometre daily per week.

a   What distance did he run during his training period?

b   If he ran at a steady speed of 13kph, what length of time did he spend running during the six weeks? (to the nearest hour).

2   During a heavyweight contest of ten rounds, each of three minutes with a one minute rest between rounds, one of the boxers is knocked out one minute fifteen seconds before the end of the eighth round.

a   How long did the contest last?

b   How many minutes and seconds of actual boxing took place?

3   A boxing promoter's main expenses for a tournament were as follows: hire of hall, seats, lighting etc., £150; payment to boxers £600; Advertising and publicity £80; other expenses £55. He sold 620 tickets @ £0·25; 380 @ £0·52½; 410 @ £0·75; 100 @ £1·05 and 110 @ £2·10. How much profit (if any) did he make?

4   An amateur boxer divided his training sessions as follows: $\frac{1}{10}$ skipping $\frac{3}{20}$ shadow boxing, $\frac{1}{15}$ light punch ball work, $\frac{1}{10}$ heavy punch ball work, $\frac{1}{3}$ running and $\frac{1}{4}$ sparring. He trained for one hour a day, five days a week. In ten weeks of training, how much time did he spend on each activity?

11 RECORDING LEAGUE FIXTURES

Keeping a record of a series of League fixtures is a simple matter provided that a chart similar to the one below is made out. The chart shows fixtures for a small League of six teams.

After each game is played, the results are written in on the left hand side of the chart and the league details worked out and entered on the right hand side. The details for the first team on the chart have already been worked out and entered for you.

Make a copy of the whole chart and then work out the final positions of each team. Remember that 2 points are scored for a win, 1 for a draw and 0 for a defeat. Remember also that if two teams have the same number of points, the position of each is determined by dividing the goals scored by the goals scored against. When this is done the team with the smaller quotient (i.e. the resulting answer), is the lower team.

	VIKINGS	SAXONS	ROMANS	NORMANS	PICTS	SCOTS	WON	LOST	DREW	GOALS FOR	GOALS AGAINST	POINTS	PLACE
VIKINGS	×	Won 3–1	Lost 0–1	Won 4–1	Won 2–0	Draw 3–3	3	1	1	12	6	7	1
SAXONS	Lost 1–3	×	Lost 0–2	Draw 3–3	Won 3–0	Won 4–0							
ROMANS	Won 1–0	Won 2–0	×	Draw 2–2	Lost 3–5	Lost 0–2							
NORMANS	Lost 1–4	Draw 3–3	Draw 2–2	×	Won 5–0	Lost 0–2							
PICTS	Lost 0–2	Lost 0–3	Won 5–3	Lost 0–5	×	Draw 4–4							
SCOTS	Draw 3–3	Lost 0–4	Won 2–0	Won 2–0	Draw 4–4	×							

1 Using a chart similar to the one just shown, work out the final laegue table for a school Basketball House League of six teams, the results of which are given below:

Results

Drake v. Hawkins	Won	26–18	
Drake v. Grenville	Won	34–12	
Drake v. Frobisher	Drew	24–24	
Drake v. Raleigh	Won	24–12	
Drake v. Howard	Won	32–14	
Grenville v. Drake	Lost	12–34	
Grenville v. Hawkins	Won	30–16	
Grenville v. Frobisher	Drew	24–24	
Grenville v. Raleigh	Lost	20–42	
Grenville v. Howard	Won	26–16	
Raleigh v. Drake	Lost	12–24	
Raleigh v. Hawkins	Won	24–12	
Raleigh v. Grenville	Won	42–20	
Raleigh v. Frobisher	Won	36–26	
Raleigh v. Howard	Won	16– 8	
Hawkins v. Drake	Lost	18–26	
Hawkins v. Grenville	Lost	16–30	
Hawkins v. Frobisher	Won	20–18	
Hawkins v. Raleigh	Lost	12–24	
Hawkins v. Howard	Won	22–20	
Frobisher v. Drake	Drew	24–24	
Frobisher v. Hawkins	Lost	18–20	
Frobisher v. Grenville	Drew	24–24	
Frobisher v. Raleigh	Lost	26–36	
Frobisher v. Howard	Won	18–10	
Howard v. Drake	Lost	14–32	
Howard v. Hawkins	Lost	20–22	
Howard v. Grenville	Lost	16–26	
Howard v. Frobisher	Lost	10–18	
Howard v. Raleigh	Lost	8–16	

12   GENERAL SPORTS QUESTIONS

1   Ski-ing

In 1966 Onni Savi of Finland ski-ed non-stop for 48 hours and covered a distance of 306 kilometres.

a   What was his average speed in kilometres per hour (kph)?

b   If he started at noon on April 19th, how many kilometres had he travelled by 9 o'clock the following morning?

2   Ice Skating

In February 1960, a Russian skater recorded a time of 39·6 seconds for a distance of 500 metres.

What was his speed in kilometres per hour (kph)?

3   Sailing

The first man to sail a boat alone around the world was Captain Joshua Slocum of America. His voyage, which covered 73,600 kilometres, took him 3 years, 2 months and 2 days, and ended on June 27th, 1898. He wrote a book about his experiences.

a   How many days did he spend on his voyage?
   (Don't forget Leap Year)

b   How many kilometres did he average each day?

4   Rowing

In 1896 two Norwegians, George Harbo and Frank Samuelson, became the first men to row across the Atlantic. Their boat measured 18 feet long and had a beam of 5 feet. Leaving New York they covered 4,920 kilometres to the Isles of Scilly in 56 days.

What was their average speed in kilometres per hour?

(Fox Photos)

Phil Read, of Britain, was the 1971 250cc World Champion. The photograph shows him leaning over into a left hand bend.

5 Motor Cycling

1 The Tourist Trophy (TT) Race for motor cyclists in the Isle of Man consists of six laps of the 60·72 kilometre circuit. A rider wins a race at an average speed 166kph.

a What is the total length of the race?

b What was the time of the winning rider?

2 At the Dayton International Speedway in America, a Canadian, Yvon du Hamel averaged 59·80 seconds for each 4 kilometre lap.

a What was his speed in kilometres per hour?

b How far does he travel in one second? (to the nearest metre).

6 Motor Racing

1 In the 24 hour Le Mans Grand Prix, a racing car averaged 185·5 kilometres per hour. What distance did the car cover in the race?

2 Sir Malcolm Campbell, father of Donald Campbell, was one of the most successful of all land speed record makers. The following figures give his records with the years in which they were made.

1924 (238kph)   1928 (331kph)   1931 (394kph)   1932 (406kph)
1933 (435kph)   1935 (442kph)   1935 (482kph)

Draw a graph to show how the records progressed over the years.

7 Walking

In 1957, David Kwan, aged 22, walked from Singapore to London. He walked for 81 weeks and averaged 35 kilometres per day. What distance did he walk?

8 Football

1 A boys' football club with 21 members wishes to raise £5·25 for a new ball. They decide to do this by selling pencils stamped with the name of the club. They buy the pencils for 15p per dozen and sell them for 2½p each. How many pencils must the club buy to cover the cost of the ball, and how many must each boy sell?

2 The record amount of money taken at an F.A. Cup Final at Wembley is £128,000 for the game between Leicester and Manchester City in 1969. Supposing that this money had been shared out between the two teams, how much (to the nearest £1) would each player have received?

3 The world record football crowd was 200,000 when Brazil played Uruguay in 1950. The gate money amounted to £125,000. What was the average admission price paid by each spectator?

9 Cricket

1 In 1920 P. G. H. Fender of Surrey scored a century in 35 minutes
In 1903 G. Jessop of Gloucester hit a double century in 120 minutes

In 1948 D. C. S. Compton of Middlesex completed a treble century in 181 minutes.

a   Draw a graph to show these batting performances.

b   If they had all been batting at the same time, how many runs would the others have scored when Fender reached his 100?

2   Brian Luckhurst made a score of 103 while playing for Kent against Somerset. His first 50 took 226 minutes, his next 53 took only 53 minutes.

a   What was his rate of scoring per minute for his first 50?

b   What was his rate of scoring for the remainder of his innings?

c   What was his rate of scoring for his whole innings?

10   Athletics

On May 6th, 1954, Roger Bannister became the first man to run a mile in under four minutes, when he achieved a time of 3 minutes 59·4 seconds. In 1967, Jim Ryun of America ran a mile in 3 minutes 51·1 seconds. If both of these athletes had been running in the same race, calculate by means of a graph, by how many yards Ryun would have beaten Bannister.

11   Golf

1   An American golfer playing on an 18 hole golf course which was 8 kilometres in length, took only 58 strokes to complete his round.

a   What was the average length of each hole?

b   What was the average length of each stroke?

2   From 1954 to the end of 1968, a great golfer earned £438,900 and won 51 tournaments. Assuming that all his money was earned at these tournaments, work out:

a   How much he earned at each hole (4 rounds each of 18 holes are usually played at major tournaments).

b   How much he earned each time he hit the ball if he averaged 65 strokes per round.

40

12 Boxing

It has been estimated that between February 21st 1947 and September 21st 1955, Rocky Marciano, ex-Heavyweight Champion of the World, earned £1,477,962. Work out his average monthly earnings during this period.

13 Cycling

In 1960, the Tour de France cycling race was run over a distance of 4,150 kilometres and was won at an average speed of 37·25kph. What was the actual cycling time of the winner to the nearest fifteen minutes?

14 Tennis

Some years ago in a singles match at Wimbledon, J. Drobny beat J. E. Patty in $4\frac{1}{4}$ hours. 93 games were played in the match. What was the average length of each game?

13 ASSOCIATION FOOTBALL

(Fox Photos)

Arsenal F.C. did the 'double' in the 1970/71 season, when they won both the League championship and the F.A. Cup. Part of this success was due to the fine goalkeeping of Bob Wilson, seen here catching a high cross cleanly.

Some Interesting Facts

The world's youngest international footballer is G. Dorval who was only fifteen years of age when he played for Brazil against Argentina in 1957.

In March 1961, Colin Jones, aged 15, of Queensferry, near Chester, is recorded as having headed a ball 3,412 times consecutively. It took him 34 minutes, 8 seconds.

In 1961 when Luiz Suarez of Barcelona joined Internazionale of Milan, he personally received a sum of £59,000.

The greatest amount of 'gate' money ever taken in Britain was that taken at the World Cup Final between England and West Germany in 1966. 93,000 spectators paid £204,804.

Exercises

1 In the matches played in the First Division one November Saturday the attendances were:

25,000	12,080	23,026	15,000	12,404	21,306
26,409	18,135	35,662	18,312	22,000	

a What is the difference between the highest and the lowest attendances?

b What was the average attendance?

2 In a football league, 2 points are scored for a win, 1 point for a draw and 0 points are scored for a defeat. Arrange the following teams in their correct order of finishing.

	PLAYED	WON	DRAWN	LOST
Derby	42	22	9	11
Leeds	42	21	15	6
Everton	42	29	8	5
Chelsea	42	21	13	8
Liverpool	42	20	11	11
Newcastle	42	17	13	12
Manchester U.	42	14	17	11
Coventry	42	19	11	12

3 Three teams are fighting for promotion. The table shows the positions on the last day of the season. In the last matches Blackpool beat Huddersfield 3–0 and Leicester won 6–1. Which two teams were promoted?

	P	W	D	L	F	A	POINTS
Huddersfield	41	26	9	6	90	45	61
Blackpool	41	25	9	7	105	50	59
Leicester	41	26	7	8	100	55	59

4 A rectangular field is 130 metres long and 90 metres wide.

a Allowing ten metres behind each goal and five metres between touch lines and the edge of the grass, what is the maximum area of the pitch?

b How far apart are the penalty spots?

c How far is the centre spot from the goal line?

14   WEIGHT LIFTING

Some Interesting Facts

Using a back lift (raising the weight off trestles) Paul Anderson, the 1956 Olympic Heavyweight Champion, raised a weight of 2,700 kilogrammes. This is roughly equal to the heaviest Rolls Royce (which weighs about 2,520 kilogrammes) and three passengers.

The greatest overhead lift ever made by a woman was that of K. Sandwena of Germany who, in 1926, lifted 127 kilogrammes – the equivalent of seven heavy typewriters.

In 1959, Chen Ching-Kai of China became the only weight-lifter to date who has ever raised over two-and-a-half times his own bodyweight (using a recognized method of lifting).

Exercises

1   On each end of a bar (which weighs 6·75kg) a weight-lifter places one 22·50kg disc, one at 9kg, two at 4kg and one at 2kg. What is the total weight he will be required to lift?

2   A weight-lifter, using three different methods, lifted the following weights: 130·50kg, 135kg and 161·50kg. What was his average lift?

3   Three weight-lifters, Smith, Jones and Ellis, compete with each other and lift the amounts given below:

Smith – 94·00kg, 94·50kg, 95·10kg, 96·70kg, 96·50kg, 97·10kg.
Jones – 93·75kg, 94·10kg, 95·20kg, 95·75kg, 96·70kg, 98·10kg.
Ellis – 94·10kg, 94·20kg, 95·00kg, 96·60kg, 96·75kg, 97·20kg.

a   What was the total weight lifted by each?

b   What was the average weight lifted by each?

c   Who won the competition and by what amount?

(Associated Press)

Bakr El Sayed Bassam of the United Arab Republic sets a new world record of 145.00kg in the Middle-Heavyweight Snatch at the Mexico Olympics.

4   A man buys a barbell set consisting of a steel bar at a cost of £1·25; four securing collars at 25p each; a key at 10p; two 20kg discs at £4·50 each; two 10kg discs at £2·10 each; two 5kg discs at £1·05 each; two 2·5kg discs at 50p each; and four 1·25kg discs at 30p each.

What is the cost of the complete set?

15 PLANNING OUT SPORTS GROUNDS

Suppose you wished to mark out on your school playing-field a number of pitches or courts of various sizes. How would you go about doing this?

It would, of course, be no use just going out with a long tape measure, a bucket of whitewash, a brush and a piece of paper with the sizes of the pitches written on it.

You would, almost certainly, not know were to start, and would waste a lot of time trying out whether or not the ground was long or wide enough for your requirements. Obviously, then, the first thing you must know is the actual size of the ground available.

This can usually be obtained from plans of the school used by the architects and builders; if such plans are not available, there is only one thing you can do. You will have to go out and measure it.

Once you know the size of the field you will have a *rough* idea as to what size of pitch or pitches you will be able to fit in the space. But there are other things to be borne in mind; for example:

1   There must be space left behind the ends of pitches and between pitches which are side by side.

2   If a cricket square is to be laid out on ground which is also used for winter games such as football, rugby or hockey, the winter pitches must not overlap the actual cricket square or it will almost certainly be ruined.

3   You must know the actual sizes of the pitches or courts you would like to mark out, but you must also be prepared to alter them slightly to fit in the space which can be used.

4   You must be careful not to have pitches too close to buildings or the boundaries of the field, otherwise you are liable to have

46

windows broken, or to waste time, and perhaps cause trouble to other people in retrieving balls which have gone into main roads or gardens of private houses.

Methods of Planning

There are two main methods of planning. These are:

1 Make a scale drawing of the ground and then draw in the pitches and courts to the same scale.

2 Make a scale drawing of the ground, then to the same scale, draw the pitches on thin cardboard. Cut these out and use them as templates on the scale drawing of the ground. Move them about until you are satisfied with the arrangement you have acheived.

Draw round the cards with a pencil. Remove the cards and write the sizes in on the plan. This second method is usually more satisfactory when the ground is an irregular shape. Here is a simple example:

A school has a rectangle playing field measuring 320 metres by 150 metres. Draw a plan of this field to include a football pitch 100 metres by 80 metres, a rugby pitch of the same size and a cricket square 25 metres by 25 metres. If possible try to keep the side and end lines of both the football and rugby pitches not less than 20 metres from the boundaries of the field.

Using squared paper and a convenient scale draw a rectangle as shown in Fig. 1 on p. 48. The pitches can be laid out in two ways; either with the lengths of the pitches running lengthways along the field, or with them running crossways. Suppose you decide to plan them lengthways, you will then need the following amount of space:

20 metres border (minimum), plus 100 metres (football pitch), plus, say, 20 metres gap, plus 25 metres (cricket square), plus 20 metres gap, plus 100 metres (rugby pitch), plus 20 metres border (minimum). This gives a minimum distance of 305 metres, which is well within the 320 metres length of the field.

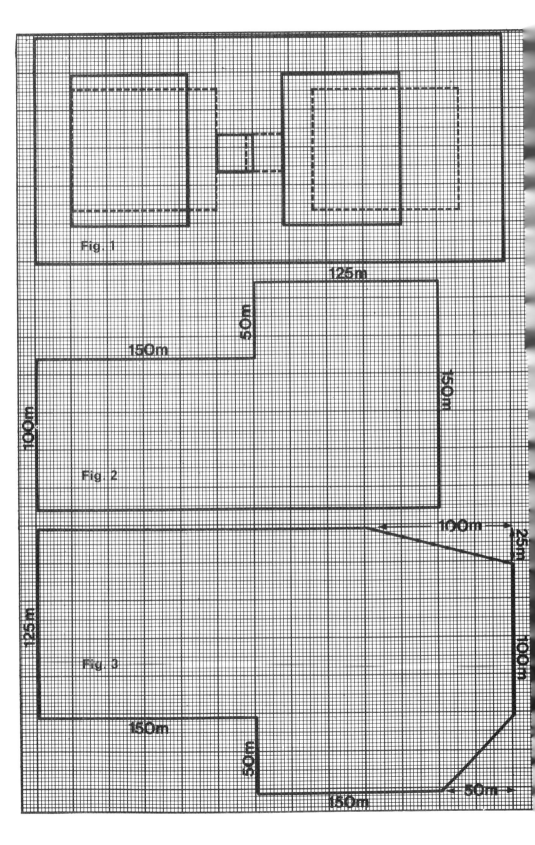

Fig. 1

125m

50m

150m

100m

150m

Fig. 2

100m

125m

Fig. 3

100m

25m

150m

50m

150m

50m

As the football and rugby pitches are only 80 metres wide you still have plenty of breadth (150 metres) to allow 35 metre borders. This layout is shown by the dotted lines in Fig. 1.

Suppose, however, you decide to lay out the pitches with their lengths running across the width of the field. You might then have the layout shown by the continuous lines in Fig. 1. This will leave you with a large unused area on the right of the field, which could be used for tennis courts or athletics or perhaps to provide a practice pitch.

On the whole, then, the second layout is probably the better one. Copy this layout on a piece of squared paper. Now using either the above method, or the cardboard template method, try to devise layouts for the areas shown below, entering the pitches and courts indicated. When you have completed your layouts, be prepared to state your reasons for the particular arrangements you have made.

Exercises

1   In Fig. 2 opposite, fit a hockey pitch (100 metres by 60 metres), a cricket square (25 metres square), and a football pitch (100 metres by 70 metres) on the area shown. Leave the largest distance possible between the playing areas and round the borders.

2   In the playing field shown in Fig. 3 try to fit the following playing areas: one large pitch not less than 110 metres by 85 metres, two small pitches (90 metres by 55 metres), one cricket square, and two tennis courts (40 metres by 20 metres). Is there a way of fitting these pitches and courts into the area and still maintaining 20 metre gaps and borders?

3   Draw a plan of your school playing field and plan out as many courts and pitches as possible.

4   Make a games layout for your school playground, then use your plan to mark out pitches and courts with chalk. Work in groups of four or five.

16 MAINTAINING SPORTS GROUNDS

Some facts

Once a sports ground has been planned and laid out the work of the groundsman really begins.

Good grass, suitable for the sport for which it is intended is one of the most difficult things to grow. It needs constant attention and the expenditure of money on machinery, seeds and fertilizer. If not carefully tended, grounds quickly become unfit for play.

Here are some example of costs taken from recent catalogues.

Lawn seed for tennis courts: from £28 per 50kg.
Grass seed for football pitches: from £11 per 50kg.
Grass fertilizer: from £1·80 to £3·00 per 50kg.
Weedkiller: from £3·00 per 50kg.
Small motor mower: from £40·00 upwards.
Large motor mower: from £300·00 upwards.

Exercises

1 A groundsman sows a tennis court, which measures 18 metres by 36 metres, with seed costing £32·00 per 50kg. He uses 30 grams per square metre.

a   How much seed does he need? (to the nearest kg).

b   What is the cost of the seed?

2   A football pitch, measuring 100 metres by 70 metres, and a rugby pitch measuring 110 metres by 70 metres, are given a 20mm top dressing of soil.

a   How many cubic metres of top dressing will be needed?

b   What will be the cost at £1.50 per cubic metre?

3   A school decides to use special Cultivated Parkland Turf for a new cricket table which is to measure 25 metres square. Each of the turves measures 1 metre by $\frac{1}{3}$ metre.

a   How many turves will be required?

b   If the turves cost £5 per 100, what will be the cost of the new cricket table?

4   To prevent worms spoiling a 20 metre square cricket table, the groundsman decides to treat the square with worm killer. If finely ground Mowrah Meal is used at the rate of 120 grams per square metre, and Mowrah Meal costs £2·50 per 50kg, what will be the cost of the treatment?

5   To keep the cricket square in good condition, a school buys the following items of equipment: a heavy roller costing £37·40; a hand fertilizer spreader costing £16·00 and a 30cm hand-mower costing £11·60.

If each of the 500 boys in the school subscribes 1p per week towards the cost of the equipment, how many weeks will it take to raise the money?

17 MOTOR RACING

Some Interesting Facts

The greatest distance ever covered in one year was 400,000 kilometres by the Frenchman, Francois Lecot, driving mainly between Paris and Monte Carlo from 22nd July 1935 to 26th July 1936. During the 370 day drive he rested only 7 days.

In 1907 the Paris newspaper, Le Matin, promoted the first long distance rally from Peking in China to Paris, a distance of 12,000 kilometres. Five cars started from Peking on June 10th and the winner arrived in Paris on August 10th.

The highest speed ever recorded for a mechanically propelled vehicle was that of Norman C. Breedlove of America, who twice covered the flying kilometre at an average speed of 961·47 kph, in his turbo-jet 'Spirit of America'. He also covered a mile at an average speed of 600·61 mph.

The most difficult race, the Targa Florio, is held in Sicily. The race consists of ten laps, each of approximately 72 kilometres, and involves severe mountain gradients, narrow rough roads and over 8,000 corners. The record time is just over 6 hours at an average speed of 128 kph.

Speed is a little difficult to understand when you see it merely written down. A motor car travelling at 640kph (about 400mph), however, will cover a distance equal to the length of two football pitches in the time you can say the word 'second'.

Exercises

1 The speed of cars is usually reckoned in kilometres per hour (kph), although you can get a better idea of speed if you think in terms of metres per second. Work out the following speeds in metres

(Nigel Snowden)

Jackie Stewart, the 1971 World Motor Racing Champion, seen cornering at the Nurbergring, Germany, in his Tyrrell-Ford.

per second then measure out the distances in the school corridor or playing field.

a 96kph   b 120kph   c 200kph   d 288kph   e 640kph

2 On a 5 kilometre circuit Jackie Stewart is averaging 1 minute 40 seconds per lap and Jack Brabham is averaging 1 minute 42 seconds. By what distance is Stewart leading:

a   after ten laps?   b   after 20 laps?

c   What is Stewart's speed in kilometres per hour?

3 In the race described in the last question, Jackie Stewart makes a pit stop lasting 50 seconds at the end of the 20th lap. After 25 laps Jack Brabham stops at the pits for 30 seconds. At the end of the 30th lap, who is leading and by how far is he leading?

4 At the start of an eighty kilometre race, one driver has difficulty starting his car and loses twenty seconds. The leading car is averaging a speed of 150kph. How fast will the late starter have to travel to dead-heat with the leading car?

5 A racing driver is testing a new car, and as part of the testing programme, he decides to drive ten laps of a 1 kilometre circuit at a speed of 100kph.

For the first two laps he averages only 60kph, but builds his speed up to an average of 100kph for the following five laps. At what speed must he drive the final three laps in order to complete the distance at the average he originally intended?

18   ROWING

Some Interesting Facts

The first English Regatta took place in about 1775 on the River Thames near Putney.

The lightest oarsman to row in a Boat Race was A. H. Higgins who was the Oxford stroke in 1882 and weighed only 9 stone 6½ pounds (60kg).

Probably the best known regatta in the world is that held annually at Henley-on-Thames. This Regatta was first held in 1839 over a course of 1 mile 550 yards.

The highest rate of rowing ever recorded in International Competition was that of the Japanese Olympic Eight at Henley in 1936, when they rowed at 56 strokes to the minute.

The greatest distance by which the Boat Race has been won was twenty lengths by Cambridge in 1900. The shortest distance was by Oxford when they won by 1 metre in 1952.

Exercises

1   The Boat Race course from Putney to Mortlake is approximately 7 kilometres in length. During a full course trial the Cambridge crew average 2 minutes 45 seconds per kilometre, rowing at 32 strokes per minute.

a   What is their time for the course?

b   How many complete strokes do they make?

c   How far (to the nearest metre) does the boat travel per stroke?

2   It is reported that the BBC pay £2,000 to broadcast the race. If the actual race lasts 18 minutes 30 seconds, how much does the

BBC pay for each minute of rowing time? If the crews were to share the money between them (which they do not), how much would each member get? (A Boat Race crew consists of eight oarsmen and a cox.)

3 The figures below show the times in minutes and seconds taken by the Oxford and Cambridge crews at ten points over the Boat Race course. Draw a graph to show the progress of the race. Use a different colour for each crew.

	1	2	3	4	5	6	7	8	9	10
Oxford	1·05	2·15	4·30	6·45	9·15	11·30	13·45	15·45	18·15	19·15
Cambridge	1·05	2·15	4·30	6·15	9·15	11·15	13·30	16·00	18·30	19·30

Mark on the graph the points: a   Where Cambridge take the lead,   b   Where Oxford draw level, and   c   Where Oxford take the lead.

4 298 boats took part in the Head of the River Race from Mortlake to Putney. The event began at 2.45 p.m. and boats started at ten-second intervals.

a   At what times did the 100th, 200th and last boats start?

If the first boat averaged 3 minutes per kilometre:

b   How long would it take to complete the course?

c   How long after it finished the course would the last boat start? (the course is 7 kilometres).

5 The table shows the weights of the Boat Race crews:

Oxford	81·4kg,	84·3kg,	85·2kg,	85·1kg,
	84·6kg,	84·8kg,	82·3kg,	81·8kg,
	57·6kg (Cox)			
Cambridge	82·3kg,	84·6kg,	85·0kg,	85·3kg,
	84·4kg,	83·8kg,	83·2kg,	82·3kg,
	57·8kg (Cox)			

a   Which is the heavier crew and by how much?

b   What is the average weight of each oarsman in each of the two crews (work to 2 decimal places).

19 CRICKET

Some Interesting Facts

The highest bowling speed ever measured is 148·8kph, which was achieved by Harold Larwood of Nottinghamshire in 1933.

The greatest number of runs scored in a season is 3,816 by Dennis Compton of Middlesex in 1947. In the same season he scored a record 18 centuries.

The most centuries made in a career is the 197 scored by Jack Hobbs between 1905 and 1934. During this period he also scored the highest total of runs–61,237.

In 1899, playing in a Junior House match at Clifton College, A. E. J. Collins scored 628 not out. The innings lasted 5 hours and 50 minutes and his side scored a total of 836.

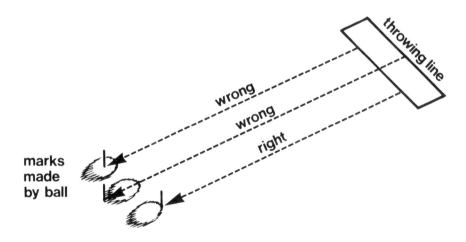

The diagram shows the correct way of measuring the length of throw in a throwing a cricket ball event. The correct length is that from the front of the throwing line to the rearmost mark of the ball.

Cricket Problems

1 The 628 not out scored by A. E. J. Collins took 5 hours and 50 minutes of batting time. What was his average scoring rate in runs per minute?

2 The longest distance a cricket ball has been thrown is 126·60 metres. Measure this distance out in your school playing field. Divide into groups of eight or ten. Each boy in the group throws a cricket ball as far as he can, and the distances measured and recorded. Find out the following:

a   The total distance thrown by each group.

b   The average throw of each group.

c   The total distance thrown by the whole class.

d   The average throw of the whole class.

3 Between 1905 and 1934 (both seasons included) Jack Hobbs of Surrey scored a total of 61,237 runs.

a   What was his average of runs per season?

b   If 21,236 were made from boundary hits and the rest were 'run' (assume 18 metres per run) what distance did Hobbs run during his career?

4 During his cricket career, Sir Donald Bradman of Australia played 338 innings for an average of 95·14. During the 1938 season he averaged 115·66 for 26 innings.

a   Calculate the total number of runs he scored during his career (to the nearest whole number).

b   Find his total score for the 1938 season, also to the nearest whole number.

20 ATHLETICS

Some Interesting Facts

In 1963, V. Brumel of Russia, cleared a height of 2·28 metres which was 42·86cm above his own height.

Robert Beamon's long jump of 8·90 metres (29ft 2½ins) at the 1968 Olympic Games in Mexico, is considered to be the greatest athletic record of all time.

At the time of writing the 'world's fastest man' is James R. Hines an American negro who won the 1968 Olympic 100 metre title in 9·89 seconds. The world's fastest woman is Wyomia Tyus of America who ran 100 metres in 11·0 seconds at the same Games.

The oldest known existing record for the Long Jump is a distance of 7·05 metres (23ft 1½ins) achieved by Chionis of Sparta in the Olympic Games of 656 B.C.

In 1882 an American, J. Saunders, ran non-stop round a track in New York for 22 hours, 49 minutes and covered a distance of approximately 204 kilometres.

Exercises

1   A very fast walking pace in 10kph.

a   How many metres will be covered in one minute?

b   What distance will be covered in 35 minutes?

c   How long will it take to cover 2 kilometres?

d   How many metres will be covered in 10 seconds?

Measure out this distance in the playground or corridor–and then time yourself over the distance. Measure the distance you walk in 10 seconds.

2 In an Olympic Games 50,000 metres walk, a competitor completed the race in 4 hours, 30 minutes. What was his average speed in kph, and, using this answer, by what distance did he beat a competitor whose time was 4 hours, 35 minutes?

3 In a Long Jump Championship, the first four competitors jumped:

(i) 8·12m   (ii) 8·11m   (iii) 8·04m   (iv) 8·00m

If a metre equals 39·37 inches, what are the distances in feet and inches jumped by each competitor?

4 A school digs a long jump pit 15m × 2m and 60cm deep. It is filled with sand to a point 10cm below ground level.

a   How many cubic metres of sand will be required?

b   What will be the cost at £2·25 per cubic metre?

A cinder run-up, 30m long by 1m wide by 15cm deep is then laid.

c   How many cubic metres of cinders will be required?

d   What will be the cost at £1·80 per cubic metre?

5 The diagram below gives the main approximate dimensions of a 400 metre running track. Draw this to a scale of 10m = 2cm.

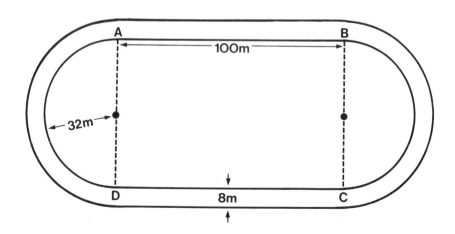

21 CRICKET

Some Interesting Facts

In 1877 Oxford University scored only 12 runs in one innings against the MCC. In 1907 Northamptonshire scored the same number of runs when playing against Gloucestershire.

The greatest number of runs scored in a single day is 721 made by the Australian tourists against Essex in 1948.

In 1938, C. I. J. Smith playing in the Middlesex v. Gloucester match, made 50 runs in 11 minutes with only 12 scoring strokes.

In 1926/27, Victoria made 1,107 runs in one innings against New South Wales, to record the highest innings ever in first class cricket.

When Kent played Gloucestershire at Dover in 1937, they scored 219 runs for 2 wickets in only 71 minutes.

R. Todd ran 4 runs wearing full cricket equipment in 12·3 seconds at Melbourne in 1940.

The highest individual score made in first class cricket is the 499 made by Hanif Mohammed at Karachi in 1959.

While playing for Warwickshire against Lancashire at Blackpool in 1959, W. J. Stewart hit 17 sixes – ten in the first innings and seven in the second.

Exercises

1 In six matches a bowler has the following performances:
Match 1 – 6 wickets for 39 runs; Match 2 – 3 for 36; Match 3 – 5 for 98; Match 4 – 4 for 19; Match 5 – 7 for 108; Match 6 – 3 for 59.

a   What is his bowling average after three matches?

b   What is his average after six matches?

2   Two batsmen are in good form. Boycott is scoring at the rate of 3 runs every $2\frac{1}{2}$ minutes and his England partner, Luckhurst, at the rate of $3\frac{1}{2}$ runs every 3 minutes.

a   What are their scores at the end of the first 90 minutes play?

b   At the end of exactly two hours Boycott is bowled out. What is his score?

c   Six minutes later, Luckhurst is caught at first slip. What is his score?

3   Each time a batsman runs a single he averages a distance of 18 metres and a time of 4 seconds. When running 'two', he runs 36 metres in 9 seconds, and when running 'three', he covers 54 metres in 14 seconds. In one innings he scores 20 singles, 14 twos and 8 threes.

a   What was the total distance he ran?

b   What was the total amount of time taken?

c   What was his average time per metre?

d   What was his average time per run?

4   Some of the world's best fast bowlers bowl at a speed of 120kph. If a bowler bowls at this speed, and the distance between his hand, when the ball is released, and the bat is 18 metres:–

a   How long has the batsman got to think before the ball reaches him?

b   How long would he have if the bowler was bowling at 72kph?

5   In a County Match, Essex start their innings 234 runs behind Middlesex and there are only 84 minutes left for play. The two opening batsmen 'go' for the runs; one scoring at the rate of 3 runs every 2 minutes, and the other at 2 runs every $1\frac{1}{2}$ minutes.
Both are not out at the end of play. What is the result of the match?

62

6 Below are given details of the first six batsmen in the batting averages in the middle of August 1970, *but they are not in their correct order*. Work out their averages to two decimal places and then put them in correct order:

	INNS.	N.O.	RUNS	AVERAGE
G. M. Turner	37	6	1776	?
B. A. Richards	26	2	1284	?
G. S. Sobers	26	7	1379	?
T. W. Graveney	27	9	927	?
C. H. Lloyd	27	3	1262	?
R. B. Kanhai	29	2	1470	?

7 The scores made in a Glamorgan v. Gloucestershire match.

GLOUCESTERSHIRE

1ST INNINGS
324

GLAMORGAN

1ST INNINGS
356 for 9 declared

2ND INNINGS		2ND INNINGS	
Nicholls	21	Lyons	9
Green	46	Jones	8
Milton	0	Khan	29
Shepherd	0	Lewis	26
Bissex	15	Davis	6
Sullivan	2	Walker (n.o.)	21
Brown	10	Cordle (n.o.)	21
Allen	16	Extras	4
Mortimore	29		
Smith	2	TOTAL	?
Meyer	1		
Extras	10	(5 wickets)	
TOTAL	?		

What was the result of the match?

8   Details are given opposite of the performances of the six leading bowlers up to August 15th 1970. They are in correct order but their averages are missing.

NAME	OVERS	MAIDENS	RUNS	WICKETS	AVERAGE
C. M. Old	403·2	103	935	55	?
D. J. Shepherd	909·3	349	1572	85	?
P. Lever	538·2	133	1361	70	?
G. D. McKenzie	567·1	145	1433	73	?
A. Ward	374·1	87	1075	53	?
R. A. Hutton	500·3	130	1265	62	?

a   Work out each bowler's average to 2 decimal places.

b   How many more balls has Shepherd bowled than Lever?

9   If each time Old bowls he takes a 20 metre run, how many kilometres has he run in bowling his 403·2 overs?

22 ROWING

Some Interesting Facts

The earliest established sculling race is the Doggett's Coat and Badge, which began in 1716. It is still rowed over the original course from London Bridge to Chelsea.

The first University Boat Race took place in 1829 at Henley and was won by Oxford.

The record time for a modern University Boat Race from Putney to Mortlake, a distance of 7 kilometres, is 17 minutes, 50 seconds by Cambridge in 1948.

The actual record for the Putney to Mortlake course was set in 1954 by the Thames' Rowing Club with 17 minutes 27 seconds.

A rowing Eight is roughly the same length as a cricket pitch, and the places occupied by the crew are designated – Bow, 2, 3, 4, 5, 6, 7, Stroke, Cox. Each oarsman has one oar only. The stroke sets the pace of the rowing and the other members of the crew try to keep in time with him. The cox plays an important part in the race, for not only does he steer the boat, but he can also indicate to the stroke when to increase the rate of rowing. At the start of a race the rate can reach 40 strokes per minute, but later usually drops to around 32/34 strokes per minute.

Exercises

1   What was the speed of the Cambridge crew (in kilometres per hour) when they set the record of 17 minutes 50 seconds for the 7 kilometre course in 1948?

2   If in this race, Cambridge rowed at an average of 30 strokes per minute :–

(Fox Photos)

Oxford lead in the 1967 *Boat Race which they eventually won. This was Oxford's last win for some time, Cambridge winning four in a row in* 1968, 1969, 1970 *and* 1971.

a   How many strokes did they make in the race?
b   How far did the boat travel at each stroke?

3   Assume both crews cover the same distance per stroke as did the boat in Question 2 b.
Cambridge row at $32\frac{1}{2}$ strokes per minute and Oxford at $31\frac{1}{2}$. How far ahead are Cambridge after ten minutes?

4 Assume a rowing Eight to be 19 metres long. In a Head of the River Race (which is rowed over the Boat Race course, but in a reverse direction), 218 crews took part.

a   How many men took part in the race?

b   If all the boats were in line and touching one another, how far from the finish of the course would be the bow of the leading boat?

c   If the boats 'go' at 30 second intervals and the first boat starts at 2 p.m., what time does the last boat start?

5   In a recent Boat Race the weights of the crew members were as follows:

Oxford: 78·50kg, 81·50kg, 84·50kg, 84·80kg, 81·50kg, 82·00kg, 79·20kg, 79·00kg and 52·50kg.

Cambridge: 76·30kg, 79·00kg, 85·50kg, 82·00kg, 81·90kg, 85·00kg, 79·50kg, 78·00kg and 56·50kg.

The Cambridge boat weighed 136kg and the Oxford boat 15kg less. The Oxford oars weighed 3·5kg each and those of Cambridge 4kg each.

a   What is the total weight of the Oxford crew?

b   What is their average weight?

c   What is the total weight of the Cambridge crew, including their boat and oars?

d   What is the difference between the total weights of Cambridge and Oxford. (Include the weights of the boats and oars).

23   CYCLING

Some Interesting Facts

The highest speed ever recorded by a cyclist is 204·768kph (127·243mph). This speed was achieved by 50-years old Jose Meiffret of France in 1962. He rode behind a windshield fitted to the back of a racing car.

In the same year, Antonio Maspes of Italy achieved an unpaced 10·6 seconds for 200 metres. This speed is equivalent to 42·21mph.

In 1965, Richard W. E. Poole rode 1,392 kilometres (870 miles) in 1 day, 23 hours, 46 minutes.

According to the Guiness Book of Records:– "Slow bicycling records came to a virtual end in 1965 when Tsugunobu Mitsuishi, aged 39, of Tokyo, Japan, stayed stationary for 5 hours, 25 minutes.

The Tour de France is probably the most severe of all cycling races. The average speed for the course of approximately 4,000 kilometres (2,500 miles) is almost 40kph (25mph).

Exercises

1   If in the Tour de France the competitors actually race for six hours each day, and the race starts on July 1st, on what date will it finish?

2   A cyclist cycles at 30kph from his home to a neighbouring town He cycles back at 20kph. What is his average speed for the whole of his journey?

3   Note: The circumference of a circle is calculated from the formula $2\pi r$. Assume π to be $\frac{22}{7}$.

(Central Press)

Eddie Merckx is one of the greatest racing cyclists riding today, having won the Tour de France several times.

The wheel of a racing bicycle has a diameter of 70cm.

a   How many times will it go round in travelling a kilometre?

b   If in one complete turn of the pedals the wheels go round $2\frac{1}{4}$ times, how many turns will be needed to travel 5km?

4   Nine members of a cycling club leave the market square of their home town and travel steadily at 24kph towards another town 16km distant. A tenth cyclist arrives at the square 5 minutes after they have left. At what speed will he have to travel to catch up with the other nine just as they reach their destination?

5   From a standing start, and paced by a motor cyclist, a Belgian cyclist covered a distance of 122km in one hour.

a   If his speed had been exactly 120kph, what would have been his speed in metres per second?

b   Measure out this distance in the corridor or playground. Calculate and measure out the distances in metres per second of the following speeds per hour:

(i)   32kph   (ii)   40kph   (iii)   100kph

24 SWIMMING AND DIVING

Some Interesting Facts

The highest dive ever made was by an American, C. V. Ireland, aged 22, who dived off the Golden Gate Bridge, San Francisco, a height of approximately 71 metres (238ft). It has been calculated that he must have been travelling at over 112kph (70mph) when he hit the water.

Miss M. Gestring of America won a Gold Medal in the 1936 Olympic Games Spring-Board Diving event when she was only 13 years of age.

The youngest person to swim the English Channel is Leonore Modell of California. She swam from France to England in 15 hours, 33 minutes, when she was only 14 years 3 months old.

The largest swimming pool in the world is the Orthlieb Pool in Casablanca, Morocco, which is 480 metres long and 75 metres wide.

The first time the English Channel was swum under water was in 1962. This feat was accomplished by Fred Baldasere, an American frogman.

Exercises

1 In diving competitions, five judges mark the competitors. To prevent any unfairness, the highest and lowest marks are eliminated, and an average taken of the remaining three. Thus, if the judges scored 5, 7, 7, 8 and 9, the 5 and 9 would be eliminated and the average of 7, 7 and 8 taken. The competitor would score 7·33.

Three dives from the end of a competition, two divers have each scored 153 points. The scores for the last three dives are:–
Black:– 1st dive: 8, 9, $6\frac{1}{2}$, $7\frac{1}{2}$, 8. 2nd dive: $5\frac{1}{2}$, 6, $6\frac{1}{2}$, 7, $7\frac{1}{2}$. 3rd dive: 9, $9\frac{1}{2}$, $8\frac{1}{2}$, 8, $8\frac{1}{2}$.
Green:– 1st dive: $7\frac{1}{2}$, $8\frac{1}{2}$, $8\frac{1}{2}$, 9, $8\frac{1}{2}$. 2nd dive: $7\frac{1}{2}$, 7, $8\frac{1}{2}$, 7, 9. 3rd dive: 6, $6\frac{1}{2}$, 7, $6\frac{1}{2}$, $7\frac{1}{2}$.

(Associated Press)

Diving is one of the most graceful of all sports. Ingebord Busch, of West Germany, dives from the high board during the Mexico Olympics of 1968.

a   What was the final score for each competitor?

b   Who won, and by how many points?

2   The times for each member of each team in a 4×1 length relay race are shown below:

North	37·5secs.	37·7secs.	38·1secs.	37·3secs.
South	37·5secs.	37·6secs.	37·5secs.	37·4secs.
East	37·5secs.	37·7secs.	37·7secs.	37·5secs.
West	37·4secs.	37·4secs.	37·2secs.	37·2secs.

a   Which team won the race and by how much?

b   What is the average time per length for each team?

c   What was the finishing order for the teams?

3   In 1968 Mike Wendon, of Australia, swam the 100 metres freestyle in 52·2 seconds. In the same year Mark Spitz swam the 100 metres butterfly in 55·6 seconds. Suppose both swimmers had been in the same race. Show, by means of a graph, by what distance Wendon would have won the race.

4   The figures below give the daily attendance at an open-air pool over a ten-day period.

Day	1	2	3	4	5	6	7	8	9	10
Children	96	130	120	132	80	130	122	108	72	101
Adults	72	84	90	108	146	130	104	150	60	72

a   Draw graphs showing the attendances of adults and children separately, and one showing the combined attendance.

b   What was the total attendance for the ten-day period?

c   What was the average daily attendance?

5   At the open-air pool mentioned in Question 4, children are charged 5p admission and adults are charged 10p.

a   What were the total takings on each day?

b   What were the takings over the ten-day period?

25 THE OLYMPIC GAMES

Some Interesting Facts

The ancient Olympic Games were held to celebrate the start of an 'Olympiad' – a period of four years. The earliest games for which records exist were held at Olympia in Greece in 776 B.C.

In the Olympic Games of 656 B.C., an athlete named Chionis of Sparta leaped approximately 6·90 metres in the Long Jump. In the 1968 Olympics in Mexico, R. Beamon of America leaped a distance of 8·90 metres. This means that in 2,600 years the best athletes in the world have only improved the record by 2 metres. This is approximately 0·8mm a year.

The ancient Olympic Games were ended in A.D. 394 by the Roman Emperor Theodosius. It is said that he did this in the advice of St. Ambrose, who thought that the games were really a pagan festival.

The modern Olympics were revived by the enthusiasm of French sportsman Baron Pierre de Coubertin. The first modern Olympics were held in Athens in 1896.

Since then the Olympics have been held in :– Paris (1900 and 1924), St. Louis, USA (1904), London (1908 and 1948), Stockholm (1912), Antwerp (1920), Amsterdam (1928), Los Angeles (1932), Berlin (1936), Helsinki (1952), Melbourne (1956), Rome (1960), Tokyo (1964) and Mexico City (1968). The 1972 Olympics will be held in Munich.

In 1920, Aileen Riggin of America won a gold medal for Spring-board Diving. She was only 13 years of age. In 1936, Marjorie Gestring, also of America and also 13 years of age, won a gold medal in the same event. In 1932, Bernard Malivoire won a gold medal as cox of the winning French coxed pairs (rowing). He was 12 years old.

Dr. Ivan Osiier of Denmark fenced for his country in the Olympic Games of 1908, 1920, 1924, 1928, 1932 and 1948, a period of 40 years.

(Associated Press)

Barbara Inkpen, of Great Britain, has changed her high-jump style to the 'Fosbury Flop'. This has enabled her to increase her personal best by several centimetres, and has made her one of the favourites for a gold medal at the 1972 Olympics at Munich.

G. Mackenzie wrestled for Britain in the Olympic Games of 1908, 1912, 1920, 1924 and 1928 (twenty years), and Mrs Dorothy Tyler also of Britain, high jumped in the Games of 1936, 1948, 1952, and 1956 (also a period of 20 years).

Exercises

1 Assuming that the rate of progress in Long Jumping continues at an average of 0·8mm per year, and knowing that the World Record at the end of 1970 was 8·90 metres, calculate in which year the record will reach: a   9·00 metres and   b   10·00 metres.

2 Knowing that the Olympic Games celebrate the beginning of an Olympiad (a period of four years) and that the 1968 Olympics marked the beginning of the 19th modern Olympiad, calculate:–

a   In which year the 50th Olympic Games will be held.

b   Which Olympiad will be celebrated in A.D. 2000.

3   It has been estimated that 250,000 people watched the 1908 Olympic Marathon Race along the route from Windsor to the gates of the White City in London (a distance of approximately 42,000 metres).

a   How many spectators were there per kilometre along the route?

b   If these spectators were equally spaced along both sides of the road, work out to the nearest centimetre how far apart they were.

4   In the 1956 Olympics the High Jump was won with a then Olympic Record of 2·12 metres. In 1968 the record was raised to 2·28 metres. Assuming that the same average improvement is maintained, draw a graph to show what heights should be cleared in the 1972 and 1980 Olympics.

5   In the 1968 Olympic Games the numbers of Gold, Silver and Bronze medals won by competitors from the first nine nations in the Medal's Table were as follows:–

	GOLD	SILVER	BRONZE
U.S.S.R.	29	32	30
Hungary	10	10	12
Japan	11	7	7
U.S.A.	45	28	34
West Germany	5	11	10
East Germany	9	9	7
Australia	5	7	5
France	7	3	5
Rumania	4	6	5

If a nation received 3 points for a gold medal, 2 points for a silver, and 1 point for a bronze, calculate the numbers of points gained by each of the above nations. Draw up a table putting them in finishing order.

The drawings on this and the next pages give details of some more pitches and courts. In each case draw the full pitch or court to a scale which will enable you to get a complete drawing on a page in your exercise book. As in the previous chapter on pitches and courts, a suitable scale is suggested in each case.

Tennis court Suggested scale: 2cm = 1 metre.

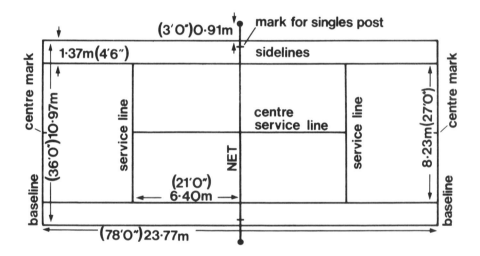

Cricket pitch Suggested scale: 2cm = 1 metre.

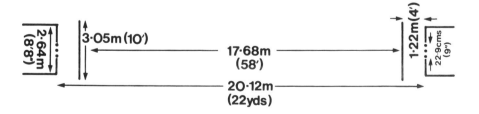

Basketball court Suggested scale: 2cm = 1 metre.

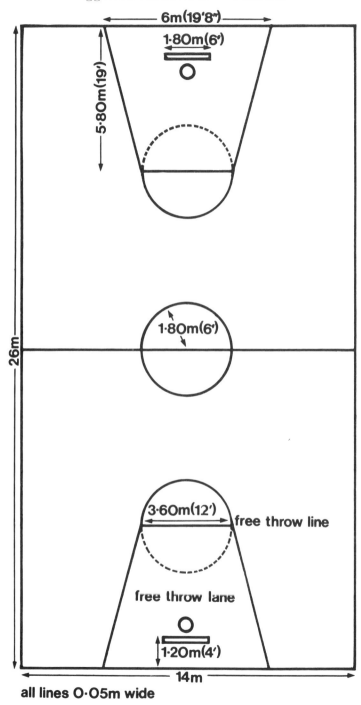

6m(19'8")

1·80m(6')

5·80m(19')

1·80m(6')

26m

3·60m(12')

free throw line

free throw lane

1·20m(4')

14m

all lines 0·05m wide

Basketball Free Throw Lane : Suggested scale: 5cm = 1 metre.

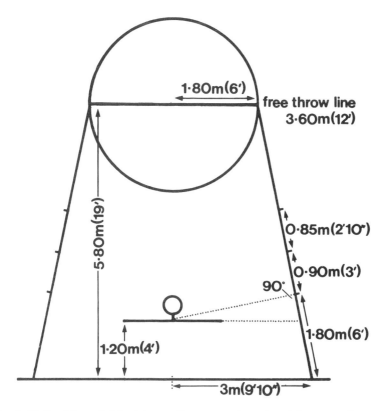

Basketball Backboard Markings : Suggested scale: 10cm = 1 metre.

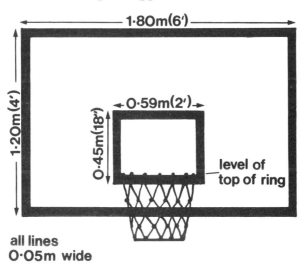

27 LAWN TENNIS

Some Interesting Facts

The modern game of lawn tennis was invented in 1874 by Major W. Wingfield, who called it 'sphairistike'! The game, however, soon became known by its modern name.

The four most important championships are those of France, Australia, America and Wimbledon. The first player to win all four in one year was Fred Perry of Great Britain, who achieved this feat in 1935.

The first woman to achieve the same distinction was Maureen Connolly (Little Mo), of America, who won the four championships in 1953.

The youngest player ever to win a Wimbledon Championship was Mrs Charlotte Dod who won the Ladies' title in 1887 when she was only 15 years of age.

The youngest male champion was Wilfred Baddeley, who was 19 when he won the Championship in 1891.

The fastest recorded service of any player was that of Lester Stoefen of America which was measured at 209·60kph.

The highest number of games ever played in a singles match at Wimbledon is 112. These were played in 1969 when Ricardo (Pancho) Gonzales beat Charles Pasarell by 22–24, 1–6, 16–14, 6–3, 11–9. The match lasted 5 hours, 12 minutes.

Exercises

1   A player serves a ball at a speed of 200kph.

a   How long does it take to reach his opponent's racquet (20m away)?

b   How long until it hits the netting 7m behind the baseline?

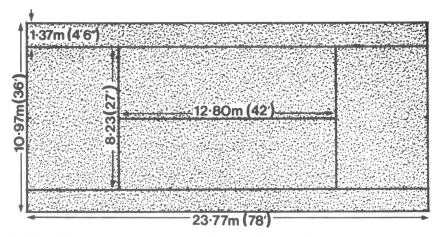

2   The diagram above shows the markings of a tennis court.

a   Draw this plan to a scale of 1cm = 2 metres.

b   What is the area of the court?

c   If all the lines were made of plastic tape, what legth of tape would be required?

d   If netting is placed all round the court, 7 metres behind each base line and four metres from each side line, what will be the total area of the ground enclosed?

3   The size of a tennis court and its surrounding grass is 40m by 20m. A groundsman, using a mowing machine which cuts a strip of grass 30cm wide, mows the grass by walking straight up and down the court.

a   How many cutting strips will be needed?

b   How many metres will he walk?

c   If he walks at a speed of 5kph, how long will it take him to mow the complete area?

4   A man decides to make a tennis court in his garden and finds that he needs the following equipment:

(i)   One set of tennis posts @ £20·25.
(ii)   One strong nylon tennis net @ £14·75.
(iii)   One net adjuster @ £0·95.

(*Central Press*)

Evonne Goolagong, an Australian, is one of the most exciting of today's players. She won Wimbledon in 1971, beating fellow Australian Margaret Court in the Final.

(iv) One set of plastic marking tapes @ £8·50.
(v) One set of nails for the tapes @ £4·75.
(vi) 120 metres of 3-metre-high netting @ £0·55 per metre run.
(vii) 3 dozen tubular steel standards @ £9·25 per dozen.
(viii) 3 dozen tubular steel top rods @ £4·30 per dozen.
(viii) 3 dozen tubular steel top rods @ £4·30 per dozen.

What is the total cost of this equipment?

5 One of the longest matches on record was that between Schroeder and Falkenburg and Gonzales and Stewart in 1949 which lasted $4\frac{3}{4}$ hours. Schroeder and Falkenburg eventually won 36–34, 3–6, 4–6, 6–4, 19–17.

a How many games were played?

b How many games did each pair win?

c What was the average time for each game?

d Using the answer for c, work out how long each set took to play.

28 CRICKET (TEST MATCHES)

Some Interesting Facts

The highest innings ever recorded in England is that made by England against Australia in the 1938 Test at the Oval, when the score was 903 for 7 wickets.

The highest individual Test Match score is 365 not out made by Garfield Sobers when playing for the West Indies against Pakistan in 1958.

The record individual score in a Test Match in England was made by Leonard Hutton (now Sir Leonard Hutton) who scored 364 when playing against Australia at the Oval in 1938.

The record number of appearances in Test Matches is held by T. G. Evans, who took part in 91 for England. P. B. H. May of England was Captain on 38 occasions, another record.

The longest Test Match on record is the one between England and South Africa in 1938-39, which was abandoned after 10 days.

T. G. Evans, playing for England against Australia at Adelaide in the 1946-47 Tests was at the wicket for 1 hour, 37 minutes before he opened his score.

Exercises

1   The slowest Test century on record was that of South African D. J. McGlew playing against Australia in 1958. He took 9 hours 5 minutes. The slowest double century scored in Test Matches was that of S. G. Barnes, playing for Australia against England in 1946-47. He took $9\frac{1}{2}$ hours to reach 200.

a   What was McGlew's rate in runs per minute?

b   What was Barnes' rate in runs per minute?

2 The figures given below show the top six batsmen in the West Indian and New Zealand teams in the 1969 Test Series. Work out their averages to two decimal places.

WEST INDIES	INNS.	N.O.	RUNS	AVERAGE
S. G. Camacho	4	0	187	?
B. F. Butcher	6	0	238	?
C. A. Davis	6	0	208	?
R. C. Fredericks	6	0	204	?
C. H. Lloyd	6	0	183	?
G. S. Sobers	6	1	150	?

NEW ZEALAND	INNS.	N.O.	RUNS	AVERAGE
G. M. Turner	4	1	126	?
B. F. Hastings	5	0	188	?
B. E. Congdon	6	1	179	?
D. R. Hadlee	3	1	55	?
B. A. G. Murray	4	1	70	?
G. T. Dowling	6	0	129	?

3 From the figures given below, work out the bowling averages for the English and New Zealand bowlers for the 1969 Test series.

ENGLAND	OVERS	MAIDENS	RUNS	WICKETS	AVERAGE
D. D. Underwood	150	70	220	24	?
R. Illingworth	101·3	43	154	10	?
A. Ward	73·5	15	210	10	?
B. L. d'Oliveira	53	21	77	2	?
B. R. Knight	35·5	8	83	2	?

NEW ZEALAND	OVERS	MAIDENS	RUNS	WICKETS	AVERAGE
B. R. Taylor	63·5	17	155	10	?
R. S. Cunis	30	6	85	5	?
D. R. Hadlee	55	10	179	6	?
H. J. Howarth	166	67	313	8	?
R. C. Motz	123·1	34	310	7	?

4   In 1970 five matches were played between England and a Rest of the World side. The records of the five best batsmen and bowlers on the Rest of the World side are given below, but they are not arranged in their correct order. In each case, work out the averages, then arrange the tables in the correct order.

BATTING	INNS.	N.O.	RUNS	AVERAGE
M. J. Proctor	9	3	292	?
E. J. Barlow	9	0	353	?
G. S. Sobers	9	1	588	?
D. L. Murray	4	0	172	?
C. H. Lloyd	9	1	400	?

BOWLING	OVERS	MAIDENS	RUNS	WICKETS	AVERAGE
G. S. Sobers	272·4	106	452	20	?
M. J. Proctor	211·1	82	359	15	?
E. J. Barlow	152	33	396	20	?
C. H. Lloyd	53	12	120	6	?
G. D. McKenzie	122·2	31	283	9	?

5   Assume that in the series described in Question 4, G. S. Sobers took a run-up of 15 metres when he bowled, M. J. Proctor one of 12·25 metres and E. J. Barlow one of 13·75 metres. From these figures and the table above work out the distance run by each of these three players whilst bowling in the series.

29   YACHTING

Some Interesting Facts

The first official yacht race in England was held on the River Thames in the year 1662. It was between Charles II and the Duke of York for a bet of £100.

The highest fully-proved speed achieved by any yacht is 16·5 knots by a schooner named 'Rainbow' in 1898.

A catamaran (which has two separate hulls) named 'Endeavour' achieved a speed of $22\frac{1}{2}$ knots over a short distance in 1955.

The race for the America's Cup originated in 1870 when a British yacht, 'Cambria' was beaten by 'Magic' of America. The holder, America, has never been defeated and still holds the Cup.

The largest private sailing yacht was the 'Sea Cloud' owned by Mrs J. E. Davies, an American. 'Sea Cloud' was a fully rigged barque and had four masts and thirty sails with a total area of 36,000 sq. ft.

'Knots'

Speed at sea is measured in knots. A knot is equivalent to one sea mile per hour. Thus, we speak of a boat travelling at 8 knots and *not* 8 knots per hour. A sea mile is 6,080 feet, but for purposes of the problems, calculate this as 100 feet per minute.

Exercises

1   The greatest distance ever covered by a sailing ship in one day was 744 kilometres by the clipper 'Champion of the Seas' in 1854.

a   What was her average speed in kilometres per hour?

b   If a kilometre is $\frac{5}{8}$ of a mile, what was her average speed in knots?

(Central Press)

The German yacht 'Rubin' competing in the Admiral's Cup in 1971. The British team, captained by Prime Minister Edward Heath in 'Morning Cloud' won the four-race series.

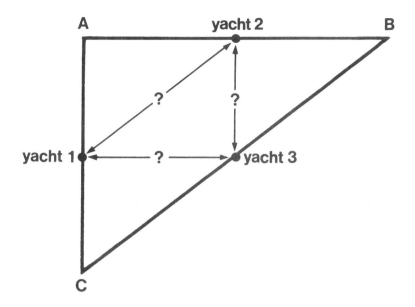

A   yacht 2   B

yacht 1   ?   yacht 3

C

2 The diagram above shows a triangular sailing course with 'legs' of 6, 8 and 10 kilometres. In the centre of each leg is a yacht. Draw the course to a scale of 2cm = 1km and carefully mark in the positions of the yachts. Find out, by measuring, the direct distance in kilometres:–

a Between yacht 1 and yacht 2.

b Between yacht 2 and yacht 3.

c Between yacht 3 and yacht 1.

3 A school decides to build a sailing dingy from prefabricated parts. The prices of the items required are as follows:
Plans–£1·70, all timber parts–£55·50, glue and fastenings–£4·25, fittings and rigging–£19·30, paints and varnishes–£5·30, suit of Terylene sails–£25·00. three buoyancy bags and fittings–£7·50, one anchor–£3·20, pair of oars–£3·50, boat cover–£9·50, launching trolley £9·25.

a What is the total cost?

b The school gets a grant of £20·00 towards the cost and raises £34·00 by means of a jumble sale. The 500 pupils share the rest of the cost equally between them. Howmuch does each pay?

88

4   The largest fully rigged sailing ship ever built was the 'Preussen'. She was 122·4 metres in length. She had five masts and 47 sails with a total of 4,444 square metres. The sail area of the dinghy in Question 3 is only 6·5 square metres.

a   If the sails of the 'Preussen' had been of suitable material, how many sets of dinghy sails could have been made from them?

b   If the material had cost the same for both vessels (i.e. £25·00 for 6·5 square metres), what would have been the cost of the 'Preussen's' sails?

5   The most expensive private yacht ever built was the 'Savarona', which cost 1½ million pounds when she was build in Germany. She carried a crew of 107 and her yearly operating costs were £208,000.

a   How much per day did it cost to run the 'Savarona'?

b   If the vessel had made a world cruise of 48,000km, lasting a full year, what would have been the average cost per kilometre?

30 ATHLETICS

Some Interesting Facts

Running last in a sprint relay in 1962 in California, Robert Hayes was timed to cover 100 yards (90 metres) in 7·8 seconds.

In Central Africa, Watussi tribesmen are credited with high jumping over 8 feet (2·4 metres).

The first time that 100 yards (90 metres) was run in under 10 seconds was in the American Championships in 1890, when John Owen had a time of 9·8 seconds.

The first athlete to clear a height of 6 feet (1·83 metres) was M. J. Brooks of England who cleared 6 feet $0\frac{1}{8}$ inches in 1876.

The first person to run a mile in under four minutes was R. G. Bannister of England. He did this at Oxford in 1954 with a time of 3 minutes, 59·4 seconds.

In 1909, two Americans ran 100 yards in 11·0 seconds. This doesn't seem particularly fast – but they were running in a three-legged race!

The record standing high Jump is 5 feet $8\frac{7}{8}$ inches (1·75 metres) by V. Einarsson of Iceland in 1961.

Exercises

1 An Olympic Games sprinter can run 100 metres in 10·0 seconds. If he could keep up this pace, how long would it take him to run:—

a   800 metres   b   1,500 metres

c   By how many metres would he beat a runner in a 1,500 metres race who recorded a time of 3 minutes, 35 seconds?

(Associated Press)

David Bedford seen during a 10,000 metre race in Poland. In this race Bedford set a new British record of 23 minutes 06·2 seconds.

2   In an International 2,000 metres race consisting of 5 laps of 400 metres, six athletes have the following lap times:–

	1ST LAP	2ND LAP	3RD LAP	4TH LAP	5TH LAP
Brown	47·2 secs	46·6 secs	46·4 secs	47·3 secs	46·2 secs
Green	47·0 secs	47·1 secs	46·5 secs	46·2 secs	45·8 secs
Black	46·9 secs	47·0 secs	46·9 secs	46·4 secs	46·0 secs
White	46·8 secs	47·1 secs	46·8 secs	46·3 secs	45·9 secs
Rose	47·1 secs	46·9 secs	46·8 secs	46·1 secs	46·1 secs
Snow	45·9 secs	46·5 secs	46·8 secs	46·4 secs	45·9 secs

a   Which athlete won the race?

b   Who was leading at the end of each lap?

c   What was the final finishing order?

d   What was the average lap time of the winner?

3 In a Marathon Race, a distance of 42,195 metres has to be covered.

a If a runner has a stride of 1 metre 20 centimetres, how many strides does he take during the race?

b If he averages 3 minutes, 15 seconds per kilometre what is his speed in metres per hour?

c What is his time (to the nearest minute) for the race?

4 An International sprinter covers 2·10 metres with each stride except for the first three strides at the beginning of a race, when he covers 1 metre, 1 metre 30 centimetres and 1 metre 70 centimetres. How many strides does he take to cover:

a 100 metres   b 200 metres   c 400 metres?

5 In the Olympic Games and in many individual countries, races have been measured in metres for many years, but only recently has Britain adopted the metric system for athletic performances.
Assuming that a metre equals 39·4 inches, find which is the greater distance in each of the following pairs:–

a 100 yards and 100 metres.

b 220 yards and 200 metres.

c 880 yards and 800 metres.

d 1 mile and 1,500 metres.

e 3 miles and 5,000 metres.